It's All Yours, Snoopy

Selected Cartoons from You've Come a Long Way, Charlie Brown, Vol 1

Charles M. Schulz

CORONET BOOKS
Hodder Fawcett, London

Copyright © 1970, 1971 by United Feature
Syndicate Inc.

First published 1975 by Fawcett Publications,
Inc, New York

Coronet Edition 1977
Second Impression 1977

Printed in Great Britain for Hodder
Fawcett Ltd., Mill Road, Dunton Green,
Sevenoaks, Kent by C. Nicholls & Company Ltd,
The Philips Park Press, Manchester

ISBN 0 340 21236 5

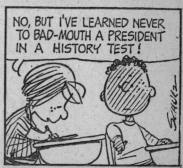

➤

I FINALLY FOUND OUT WHAT THAT STUPID BIRD'S NAME IS...

YOU'LL NEVER BELIEVE IT..

WOODSTOCK!

Dear Valentine,

I love you.

Whoever you are.

THERE'S OUR MAILBOX...WOULDN'T IT BE GREAT IF THERE WAS A VALENTINE IN THERE FOR ME FROM THAT LITTLE RED-HAIRED GIRL?

WOULDN'T IT BE GREAT IF IT WAS A REAL FANCY ONE WITH ALL SORTS OF HEARTS ALL OVER IT AND LACE AND EVERYTHING?

A Report on George Washington
George Washington
was a great man.

He probably had some faults, but if he did, I don't know what they were.

Which is just as well.

Schulz

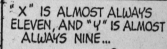

YES, MA'AM...THAT'S MY BOOK REPORT..

WHAT ARE THE ODDS ON A LITTLE LOVE AND UNDERSTANDING?

WHEN YOU'VE JUST COME HOME
FROM WORM SCHOOL, THERE'S
A LOT TO TALK ABOUT

➡→

➤

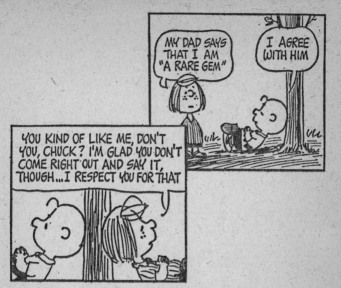

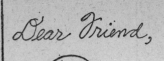
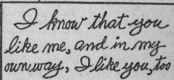

CARRYOUT

OH, I'M SORRY, MRS. BARTLEY..I DIDN'T MEAN TO STARTLE YOU..

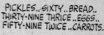

GOOD MORNING MRS. LOCKHART.. HOW ARE YOU TODAY? HOW'S ALL THE FAMILY?

PICKLES..SIXTY..BREAD.. THIRTY-NINE THRICE..EGGS.. FIFTY-NINE TWICE..CARROTS..

HEY, FRED, HOW MUCH ON THE CARROTS?

DID YOU HAVE ANY BOTTLES, MRS. LOCKHART? THANK YOU

GOOD MORNING, MRS. MENDELSON..HAS YOUR HUSBAND FOUND A JOB YET? HOW WAS YOUR TRIP TO HAWAII?

BREAD..THIRTY-NINE EIGHT TIMES..SOUP..TWO FOR TWENTY-NINE...TEN CANS... COFFEE... A DOLLAR SEVENTY-EIGHT... TUNA..THIRTY-NINE TWICE..

SIGH # SEVEN HOURS AND FORTY MINUTES TO GO... GOOD MORNING, MRS. ALBO..HOW ARE YOU TODAY, SWEETIE?

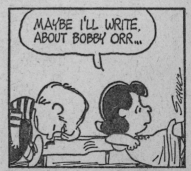

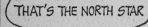

IF YOU THINK ABOUT SOMETHING AT THREE O'CLOCK IN THE MORNING AND THEN AGAIN AT NOON THE NEXT DAY, YOU GET DIFFERENT ANSWERS..

HERE, CHARLIE BROWN... SIGN THIS PETITION!

WHAT'S IT FOR?

DON'T BE SO WISHY-WASHY.. JUST SIGN IT!

WANTING TO KNOW WHAT YOU'RE SIGNING IS NOT BEING WISHY-WASHY!

WHY ARE YOU SO CRABBY?

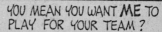

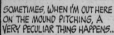

SOMETIMES, WHEN I'M OUT HERE ON THE MOUND PITCHING, A VERY PECULIAR THING HAPPENS..

SOMETIMES I START THINKING ABOUT THAT LITTLE RED-HAIRED GIRL..

HERE I AM, SURROUNDED BY KIDS PLAYING BASEBALL..EVERYONE IS YELLING AND SCREAMING AND RUNNING AROUND, AND WHAT AM I DOING? I'M PITCHING, BUT I'M THINKING ABOUT HER

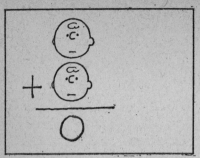

THAT'S LIFE...YOU SET YOUR ALARM FOR SIX O'CLOCK, AND THE WORM SETS HIS FOR FIVE-THIRTY

ONE FINGER WILL MEAN A STRAIGHT BALL, TWO FINGERS WILL MEAN A STRAIGHT BALL, THREE FINGERS WILL MEAN A STRAIGHT BALL AND FOUR FINGERS WILL MEAN A STRAIGHT BALL....

I HAVE A VERY SARCASTIC CATCHER

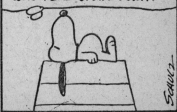

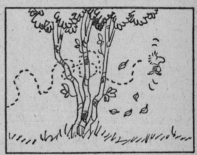

BONK!

ALL THIS AND SNOOPY, TOO

All these books are available at your local bookshop or newsagent, or can be ordered direct from the publisher. Just tick the titles you want and fill in the form below.
Prices and availability subject to change without notice.

....

CORONET BOOKS, P.O. Box 11, Falmouth, Cornwall.
Please send cheque or postal order, and allow the following for postage and packing:
U.K. – One book 22p plus 10p per copy for each additional book ordered, up to a maximum of 82p.
B.F.P.O. and EIRE – 22p for the first book plus 10p per copy for the next 6 books, thereafter 4p per book.
OTHER OVERSEAS CUSTOMERS – 30p for the first book and 10p per copy for each additional book.

Name ....

Address..

....